MENSA VISUAL TRICKS

Isabella Riedler, Gyles Brandreth, Michael A. DiSpezio, Katherine Joyce & Charles H. Paraquin

**OFFICIAL MENSA
PUZZLE BOOK**

Main Street
A division of Sterling Publishing Co., Inc.
New York

Library of Congress Cataloging-in-Publication Data Available

2 4 6 8 10 9 7 5 3 1

The collection is excerpted from the following Sterling titles:

Tricky Puzzles for Clever Kids, by Isabella Riedler © 1999 Arena Verlag GmbH
under the title *Ratsel Rakete*
The Little Giant® Book of Cool Optical Illusions, by Gyles Brandreth,
Michael A. DiSpezio, Katherine Joyce, & Charles H. Paraquin
© 2002 Sterling Publishing Co., Inc.

Published by Sterling Publishing Co., Inc.
387 Park Avenue South, New York, NY 10016
© 2004 by Sterling Publishing Co., Inc.
Distributed in Canada by Sterling Publishing

^c/o Canadian Manda Group, One Atlantic Avenue, Suite 105
Toronto, Ontario, Canada M6K 3E7
Distributed in Great Britain and Europe by Chris Lloyd at Orca Book
Services, Stanley House, Fleets Lane, Poole BH15 3AJ, England
Distributed in Australia by Capricorn Link (Australia) Pty. Ltd.
P.O. Box 704, Windsor, NSW 2756, Australia

Printed in United States of America

ISBN 1-4027-1644-3

CONTENTS

Introduction 4

Optical Puzzles 7

Answers 118

Optical Illusions 151

Answers 261

Index 282

INTRODUCTION

Optical illusions take advantage of basic weaknesses in the visual system. Playing with these illusions helps to sharpen your visual thinking skills. Would you like to know more?

Whenever you "see" an object, light rays are actually reflected from the object into your eye, past the protective outer cornea, and through a tiny opening called the pupil. The pupil is the dark spot in the middle of the iris. And the iris is the muscular disk that changes the size of the tiny opening, depending on the brightness of a scene. (The pigments in the iris determine your eye color!)

Behind the pupil and the iris is a lens that is so flexible, you can focus on near and far objects, and even see things that you're not really focusing on.

The light rays then pass through your jelly-like eyeball and onto the retina—a screen at the back of your eye. The retina is made up of little cellular structures called rods and cones, which are sensitive to light and color. From there, a pathway called the optic nerve relays the image to the brain.

Your brain interprets this information as a picture—ah, but not always "correctly"! There are no light-sensitive cells where the retina and optic nerve connect, creating a blind spot. And sometimes, the brain simply takes short cuts in processing information.

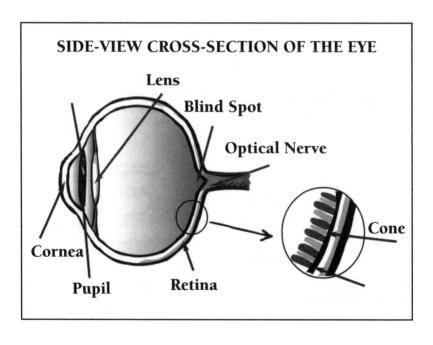

SIDE-VIEW CROSS-SECTION OF THE EYE

Lens

Blind Spot

Optical Nerve

Cone

Cornea

Pupil

Retina

So, usually we see what we expect to see. But sometimes our perception lets us down, and we perceive something to be so that isn't really so!

That should happen to you quite a few times as you look through this book, because optical illusions very often manage to fool your perception. And then you begin to wonder—*is seeing really believing?!*

OPTICAL PUZZLES

DOWN THE SLIDE

In each picture, 3 children are going down the slide. If you look carefully, you'll see that there are only 8

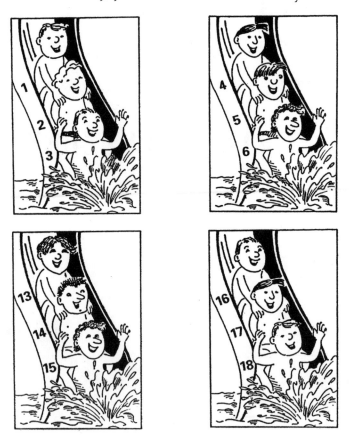

different children and you are seeing each one 3 times.
Can you find each "triplet"?

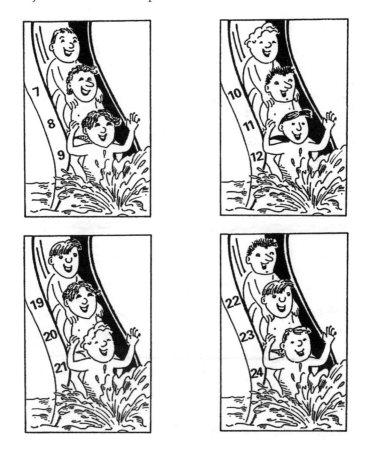

SWIMMING MARATHON

All swimmers are swimming to the right—except one!
Can you find her?

A HUGE HOLE

It was spring when Richard took his tent out of the closet and set it up. He was shocked to see that moths had eaten a huge hole out of it during the winter.

How many boxes did the moths eat?

WHO IS FLYING WHERE?

The 3 planes below are flying to 3 different cities.
Where is each one landing?

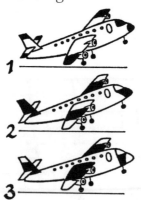

1 _____

2 _____

3 _____

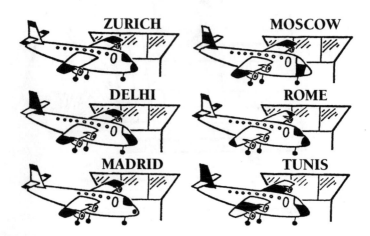

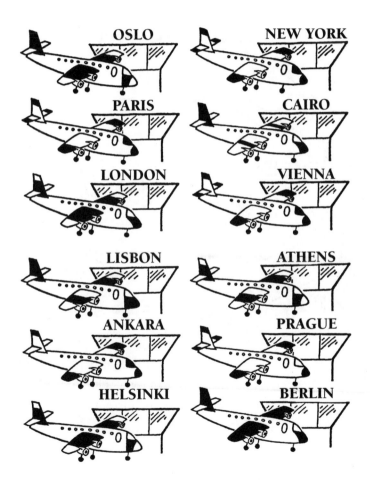

OSLO

NEW YORK

PARIS

CAIRO

LONDON

VIENNA

LISBON

ATHENS

ANKARA

PRAGUE

HELSINKI

BERLIN

WHERE IS MY WIFE?

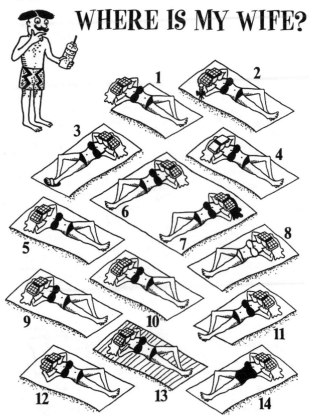

Her black bikini has straps. The book she is reading has a black spine and a checkerboard cover. Her hair is light, long and not tied back. She is lying all by herself on a towel that is white and longer than she is tall. She is barefoot.

Which one is she?

LONG TONGUES

Which chameleon is licking the ice cream cone?

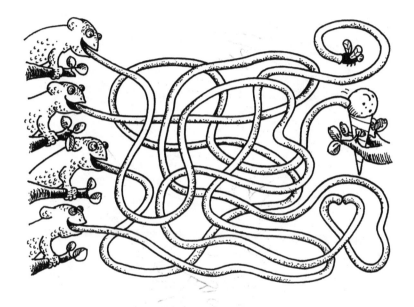

LOOKING FOR THE BOOMERANG

Tom's boomerang is stuck between the clothes hangers. Will you help him find it?

ON A GONDOLA IN VENICE

Which canal will get the gondola to the palace?

KITE FESTIVAL

The owners have written numbers from 1 to 9 on the kites below. When you add up the numbers that appear on each kite and then compare the totals, you'll know which kite is flying on the longest string.

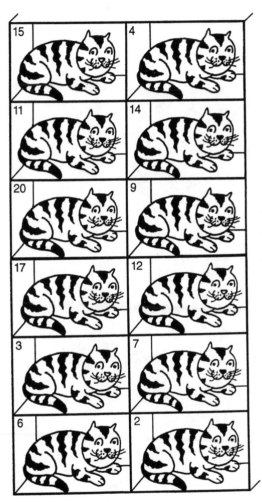

FOUR TRIPLETS

There are 4 triplets in this group of 12 cats. Can you find them? If you want to check your answer, the numbers of each set of triplets will always add up to 30.

CAMELS

Can you find the complete camel?

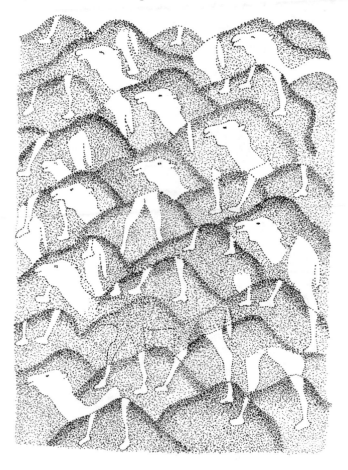

WILD RIVER

Hubert lost his paddle going down the river in his kayak. Where is it?

HALF A CROWN

Show the king which 1 of the 4 parts will complete his crown perfectly.

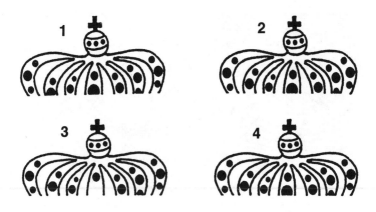

NEW EYEGLASSES

Which 2 of these 17 lenses can the owl insert into its frame so that it can see just as well with both eyes? The same mouse has to appear in both lenses.

HAT HEAVEN

A strong wind blew the chef's hat into the clouds.
Where is it?

WASH DAY

Find 7 differences between these 2 pictures before the laundry dries!

MYSTERIOUS REQUEST

The passenger in this taxi will not tell the driver her destination. Instead, she says:

"Go straight for a few blocks. Then make a left twice, then a right twice, then make a left and then a right and again a left."

Which house does the woman want to get to?

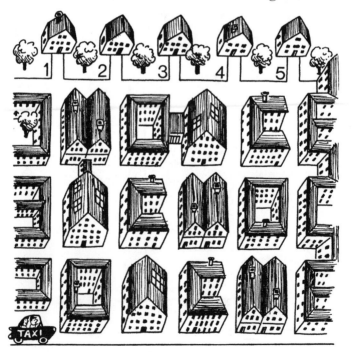

ROCK CLIMBING

Can you find 15 differences in these 2 pictures—before the rock climber reaches the top of the mountain?

GREETINGS FROM THE WOODCHUCK

Which of the 8 views through the telescope accurately shows the cute little woodchuck at the top of the mountain?

WHERE IS THE ?

HOW OLD IS THIS TREE?

On this tree are numbers from 1 to 20. Wait a minute!
Some of those numbers are missing! If you write the
missing numbers into the row of boxes below and then
add them up, the total that you get will tell you how
old the tree is.

WHICH 6 OBJECTS...

Which 6 objects do not appear twice?

HIBERNATION

Which bear lives in this cave? To find out, compare the outlines of the bears with the outline at the entrance of the cave.

GATHERING OF THE RAVENS

Where are the 6 rooks among all these ravens? Rooks are birds that have a bare patch of skin at the base of their bills, instead of the black.

LOOKING FOR FOOTPRINTS

The blackbird landed between the branches 3 times, leaving its footprints. Where are these spots?

HOME OF THE FOUNTAIN PEN

Into which of the 4 cases does the fountain pen fit?

IN THE HAT SHOP

In the picture on top, Billy is going into the shop to buy a new hat. He tries on all the hats and caps and puts them back in a different spot. He buys one of the

hats, and the clerk replaces it with another hat. Which hat does Billy take with him and which one is new?

POTATO STAMP

Mimi made this stamp out of a potato. On which of these 4 pieces of paper has Mimi put her stamp?

CRAZY ABOUT BOOKMARKS

Is a bookmark sticking out of every page of these books? Not quite! Look in each book for the page that has no bookmark sticking out! If you cannot find it by just using your eyes, a ruler may help.

MANY GREAT-SMELLING GINGERBREADS

Can you find 4 cards (aces) and 3 dice hidden among these sweets?

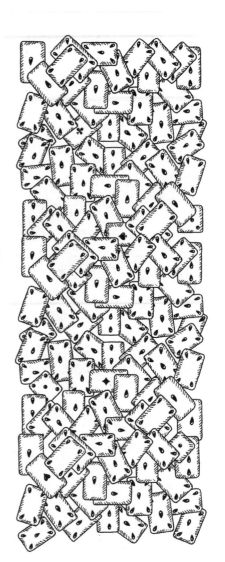

GINGERBREAD DOMINOES

Charlie is supposed to play dominoes with these 9 gingerbreads, beginning with 6/6. If he can match up the pieces into a sequence so that just one remains, he is allowed to eat it. Which one will he get to eat?

HIDDEN GIFTS

Which of these 4 piles of gifts is Santa carrying under his hat?

FROM FALL TO WINTER

Put these New England pictures into the correct sequence, beginning with picture #2, and follow the seasons. Which picture does not fit?

STAR POINTS

Monica made the stars in the left-hand picture herself,
and the ones in the right picture were made by Mark.

Who made the star with the fewest points and who made the one with the most points?

WHERE IS THE REINDEER?

SELF-SERVICE

Which bird picked up its package from which Santa Claus?

DECORATING
THE CHRISTMAS TREE

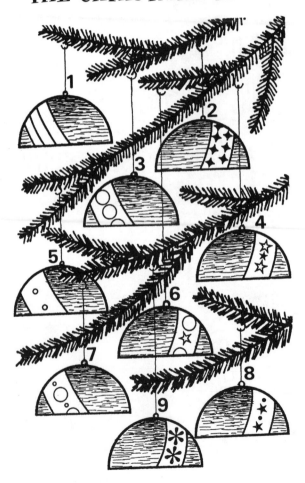

Match up the Christmas ornaments on the left with those on the right. Also when you write the letters that are next to the ornaments (in the sequence 1 to 9), you'll find the name of one of the figures in most every nativity scene.

THE SNOWMAN'S HAT

Which of the 15 pots is on the head of the snowman?

A SWEET JOB

You are allowed to take 5 cookies from this plate, but only those whose numbers add up to 100.

Which 5 are those?

COOKIE DOUGH

The cookies on the baking sheet (in the center) all come from one of these batches of dough. Which one?

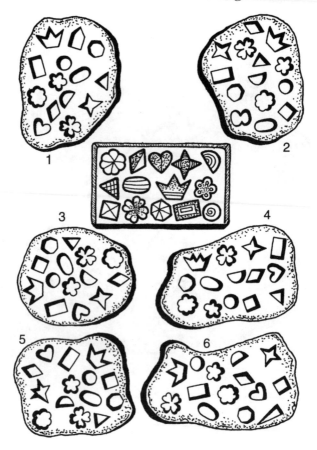

JOHN'S CHRISTMAS WISH

Which one of the 14 guitars is in the wrapped package?

AMAZING VIOLINS

Snails have been used to create 3 of these violins!
Which are they?

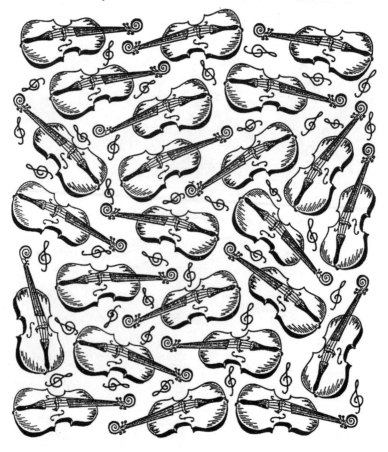

THE LEAPING SEAL

Which of the 4 seals has already jumped through the thin ice? Compare the heads and bodies of the seals with the shape that you see in the ice!

SKATING ELKS

Can you find 20 differences between these 2 pictures before one of the elk skids?

FOUR SKATERS

Which 2 penguins skated the circles around the 2 seals?

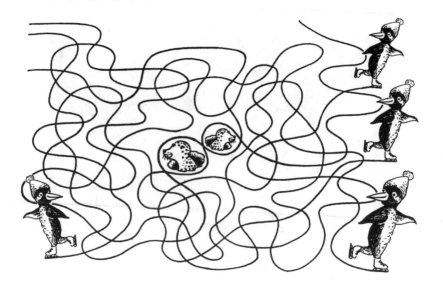

THE SLED

Can you find 7 differences between the 2 pictures?

IDENTICAL SQUARES

As you see, the drawing of the large hockey-playing snowman (left) has been broken down into 40 squares. The drawing below has also been broken into squares—35 of them. In the 2 drawings, 3 of the boxes are exactly the same—although the sizes are different. Can you find these 3 pairs?

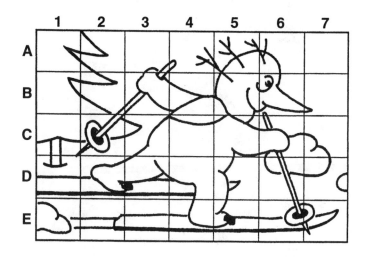

TREE SLALOM

The trees on this course take the place of poles. From start to finish, the runners may only go around trees that are the same type as the ones at their starting point. When you follow their tracks and try to connect them, you'll find out which is the only skier to run the slalom without making a mistake.

WHO SHOT THE GOAL?

THE BIG SNOWBALL FIGHT

There are 2 teams—one on the left, one on the right.
The kids on the left throw snowballs at the kids on the

Greg

Peter

Eve

Bob

Susanne

George

right and vice versa. Find out which picture-pairs fit together and you'll know who hit whom!

Will

Ken

Phillip

Alice

Hannah

Paul

DOWNHILL SKIERS

Which of these "ski-bunnies" fit exactly into the outlines?

LET'S HIT THE SLOPES

Normally, 1 person carries 1 pair of skis. But here, somewhere, 2 people together are carrying 1 pair. Where are those 2?

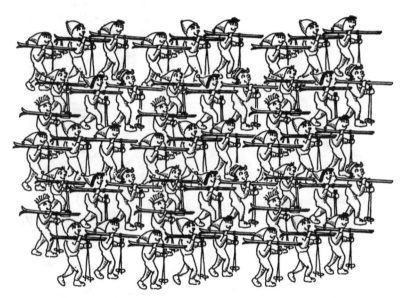

SIX SNOWBALLS

Roberto is rolling down the mountain in 1 of these 6 snowballs. Which one?

SNOWMAN MOUNTAIN

How many snowmen can you build from all those spare parts that make up the mountain? The fellow at the top is your model, and he doesn't count.

BANK ROBBERY

Can you find 15 differences between the 2 pictures—
before the bank robber makes his getaway?

CARNIVAL GAME

Into which 4 holes do you have to throw a ball in order to score 60 points exactly?

RRRROCKET

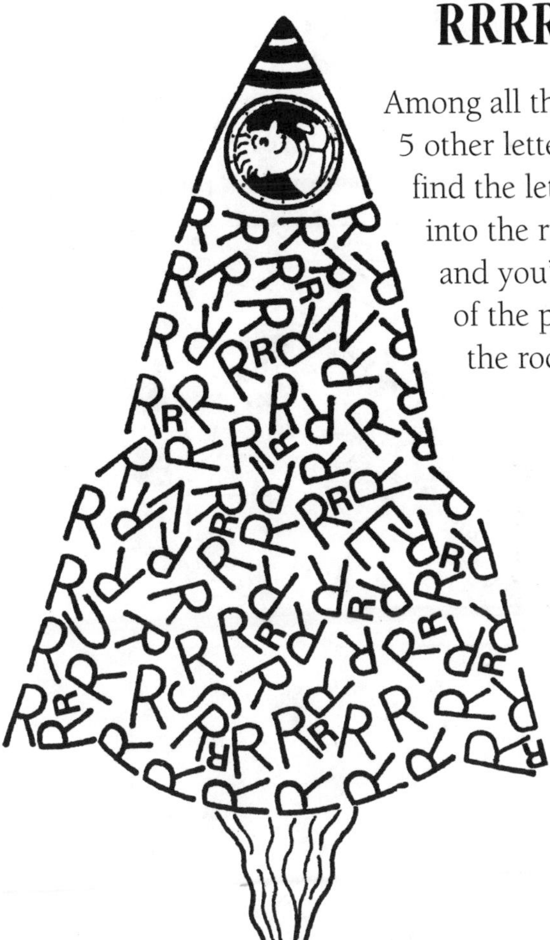

Among all those Rs, there are
5 other letters. When you
find the letters, put them
into the right sequence
and you'll find the name
of the planet to which
the rocket is flying.

LUCKY HIT

In the picture on top, 7 kids are throwing snowballs over the house. In the picture below, you see where they land. Who hit the person who is shoveling the snow?

THE JESTER'S HAT

Which of the 7 decorations is not on the jester's hat?

WHERE IS MY MASK?

My mask has five pointy light-colored feathers. The mouth is open, the eyes are narrow, and there's a black spot on the nose. The beard does not have a black spot. The eyebrows are light-colored and the cheeks are dark.

CALCULATING WITH 2 CLOWNS

When you add up all the numbers in each clown, you'll find out the number of costume parties that each of them has attended during the last 10 years! (6s and 9s are not upside down).

THE RUSSIAN DOLL

Put a piece of tracing paper—or any paper you can see through—over the picture and draw the doll. Don't go over any line twice.

BUTTERFLIES

Which butterfly flew out of the flower?

THREE FACES

In the 2 pictures, below and opposite, 3 faces do not appear in both pictures. Which 3?

THROUGH THE HEDGE

Show the caterpillar the path through the hedge! It must not come out next to the bird, but on the left side of the hedge.

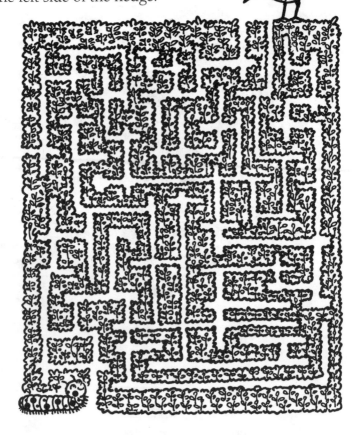

ELEPHANT WATCH

Can you find 7 differences between the 2 pictures—before the commercial?

THE CENTIPEDE

The centipede can hold this pose for only 7 minutes more. After that, it will become too exhausting.

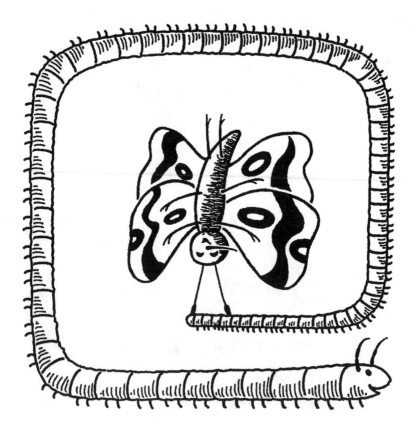

Before that time, can you find 10 differences between the 2 pictures?

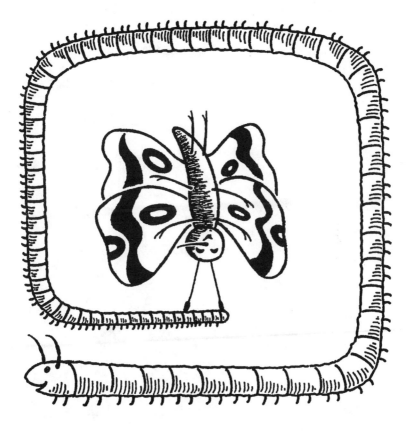

EGG FRAUD

It looks as if all 18 animals hatched. But anyone who has some knowledge of zoology knows that only 3 of them hatch! Do you know this trio?

RABBIT COMPANY

Can you find the 1 rabbit whose ear shape, whiskers, hind legs, and basket are not repeated in any of the other 6 rabbits?

WHERE ARE THE RABBITS?

Where are the 5 rabbits with 1 ear? The 5 rabbits with 3 ears?

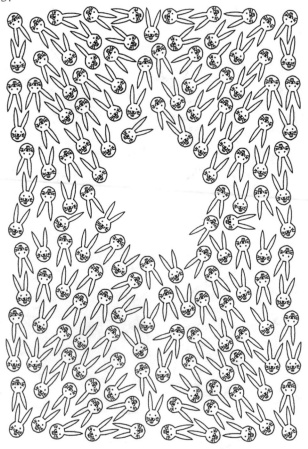

LOOK FOR 15 DIFFERENCES!

A MUSEUM PIECE

If you want to know how old this vase is, you need to add up all the numbers! (6s and 9s are not upside down).

THE GIANT EGG

An artist painted this egg beautifully. But when you look closely, you will see one pattern in each of the 8 rows that does not fit. Can you find these mistakes?

PAINTING EASTER EGGS

After these Easter eggs were decorated, these 4 kids added their own special designs to some of them.

Paula painted her freckles, Jeff painted one of his buttons, David painted his eyeglasses, and Vickie painted the bow in her hair. The kids "signed" 12 eggs altogether. Can you find them—and tell how many eggs each kid signed?

Paula

Jeff

FROG TUBA

Which mouthpiece must the frog blow into so that a
sound comes out of the funnel?

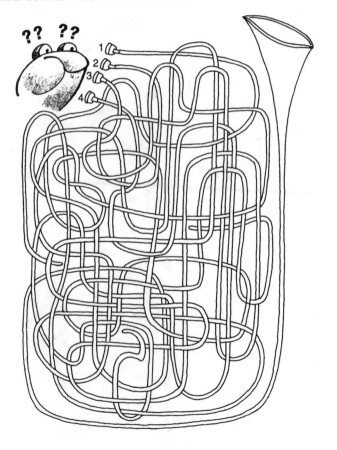

WHO IS RIDING?

When you connect the lines, which are interrupted by the bushes, you will see who is riding on whom!

EXCHANGING EARS

As you know, rabbits always have 2 identical ears; but obviously, the illustrator of these rabbits has never seen a real rabbit. Can you find ears that match for each rabbit? (One letter and one number always go together.)

WHO IS OLDER?

When you count all the numbers in these 2 steam engines, you'll find out which one is older. (6s and 9s are not upside down.)

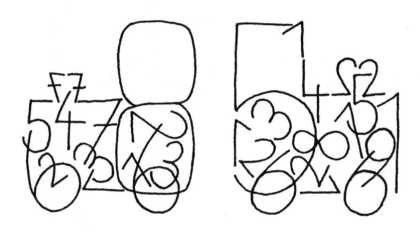

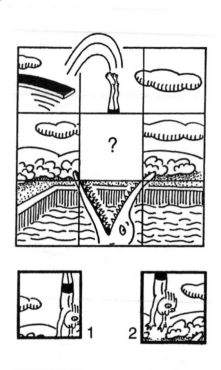

GOING SWIMMING

Which numbered section is missing in the picture at the top?

1

2

3

4

5

6

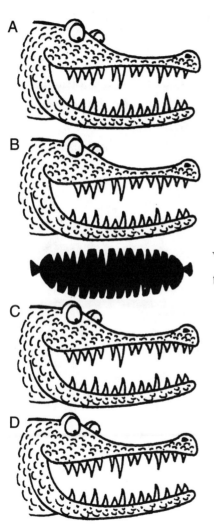

CROCODILE SNACK

Which crocodile bit into the sausage?

CROCODILE IN LOVE

With the help of the information in the bubble, can you discover the crocodile on the right side that is exactly what this romantic crocodile has in mind?

My dream partner must not have a gap in his teeth. His jaws must be the same length, and he mustn't be cross-eyed. His tail must be pointy, and I would love it if his forefoot had four claws!

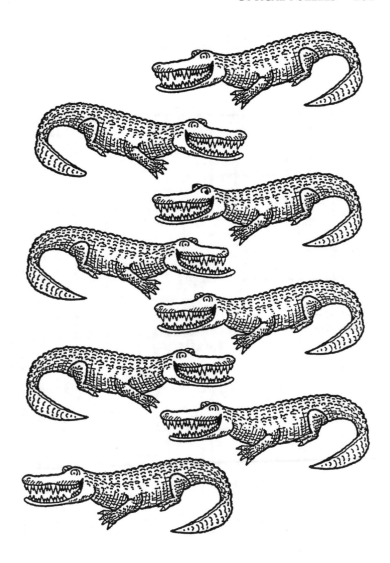

THE THIRSTY BIKER

Which of the 4 paths will lead Gary to the lemonade?

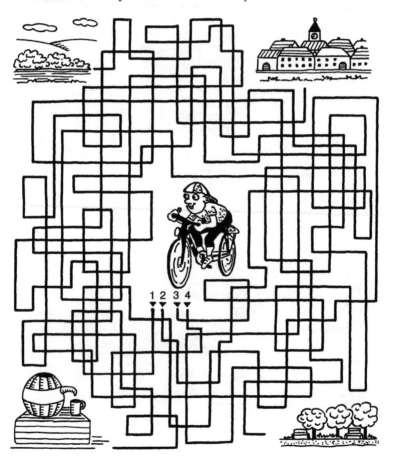

SCHOOL BUS

Which of the 5 parts belongs to the bus?

SORTING LUGGAGE

Which 6 pieces of luggage do not appear in both pictures?

EAR SCIENCE

Give every pair of ears to the right animal. When you do, there will be one pair of ears left. They belong to an animal that likes to see the world upside down. What is it called?

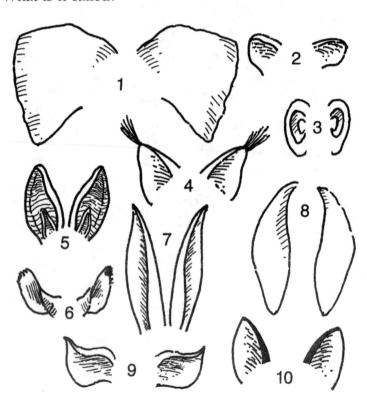

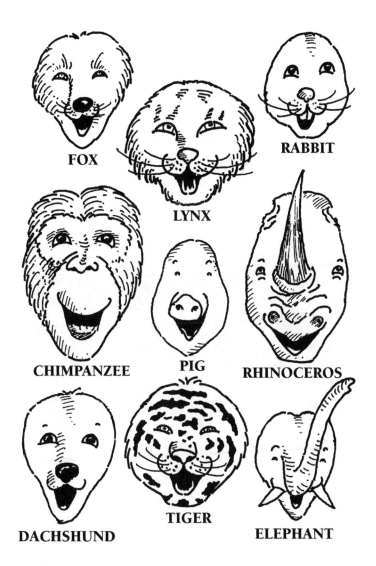

FOX

LYNX

RABBIT

CHIMPANZEE

PIG

RHINOCEROS

DACHSHUND

TIGER

ELEPHANT

WHO WON?

At the end of the soccer game, the field players of both teams decided to shoot at a goal at the same time. One team used only white balls; the other team, only black balls. Even though all shots hit the goal, the only balls that count are the ones that add up to 50. So you need to find out how many balls of each color add up to exactly 50 points. Then you'll know who scored the most balls—and won!

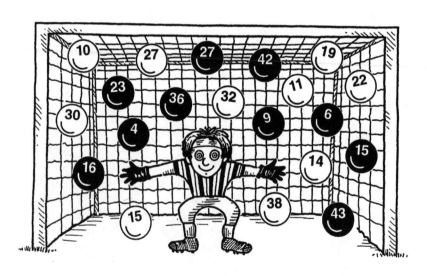

ATHLETES

The picture at the top shows 11 athletes in action, and the bottom picture shows pieces of athletic equipment. What pairs belong together? Match up the letters and numbers. Who will be left without any equipment at all?

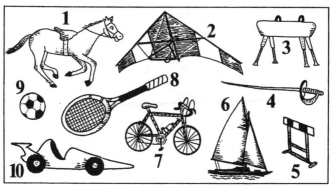

NUMBER SPECTACULAR

Add up all numbers and divide the sum by the number that occurs least! Multiply the result by the number that occurs most. (6s and 9s are not upside down.) What is the answer?

÷	=	X	=

LONE FISH

23 of the 24 fish in each aquarium appear in both tanks. But each tank has one loner. Can you find them?

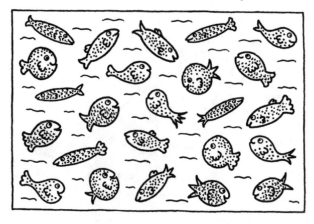

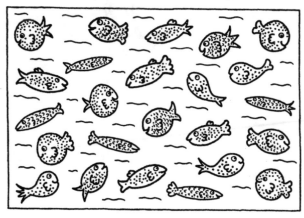

THE BIRD

What did the bird do most? Eat cherries, or sing songs?

WHO LIVES HERE?

Compare the shapes of the 6 dogs with the black drawing in the doghouse, and you'll know who lives in it.

TWINS IN THE POND

In the ponds below, 2 of the children are twins. And 2 of the ponds also look the same. Can you find the twin children—and the twin ponds?

THE KNIGHT'S SHIELD

Fill in the black areas needed on the shield of the knight at the bottom right, so that it follows the same kind of sequence as in the row above.

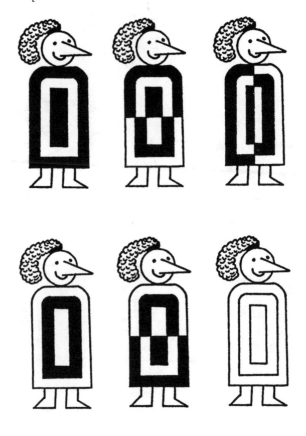

THE TOWER

This military tower was built from 11 of these 12 pieces. Look for the spots on the wall that match every piece exactly. Which piece is left over?

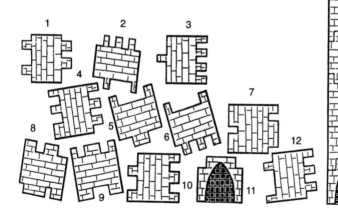

ANSWERS

Down the Slide

The following children are triplets:

1, 18, 24	5, 19, 23
2, 10, 21	6, 8, 15
3, 7, 16	9, 13, 20
4, 12, 17	11, 14, 22

Swimming Marathon

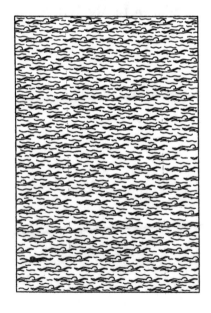

A Huge Hole

The moths ate 47 boxes.

Who Is Flying Where?

Plane 1: New York

Plane 2: Tunis

Plane 3: Helsinki

Where Is My Wife?

She is #9.

Long Tongues

The second from the bottom.

Looking for the Boomerang

On a Gondola in Venice

Canal #3.

Kite Festival

The kite with the triangular eyes is flying on the longest string.

Four Triplets

The triplets are: 3, 12, 15; 4, 6, 20; 2, 11, 17; and 7, 9, 14.

Camels

Wild River

Half a Crown

#4 will do it.

New Eyeglasses

#14 and 15.

Hat Heaven

Wash Day

Mysterious Request

House #5.

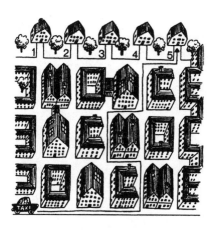

Rock Climbing

Greetings from the Woodchuck

View #8.

Where is the  ?

How Old Is This Tree?

$2 + 5 + 9 + 11 + 13 = 40$

The tree is 40 years old.

Which 6 Objects Do Not Appear Twice?

Folder, ear of corn, jug, wine glass, potato, walking stick.

Hibernation

Bear #5.

Gathering of the Ravens

Looking for Footprints

In the Hat Shop

Picture on top: Billy takes the hat that is third from the left in the bottom row.

Picture below: The fourth hat from the left in the top row is the one that the clerk brought out of the back room to fill the hat stand.

Home of the Fountain Pen

Case d.

Potato Stamp

On paper #4.

Crazy About Bookmarks

Top book: The sixth page from the top.

Book in the middle: The sixth page from the bottom.

Bottom book: The fourth page from the bottom.

Many Great-Smelling Gingerbreads

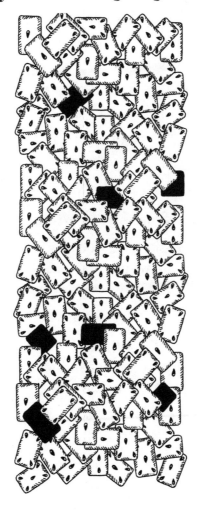

Gingerbread Dominoes

Charlie will be allowed to eat gingerbread #2/4.

It will work like this: 6/6 – 6/5 – 5/0 – 0/2 – 2/3 – 3/4 – 4/1 – 1/6.

Or like this: 6/6 – 6/1 – 1/4 – 4/3 – 3/2 – 2/0 – 0/5 – 5/6.

Hidden Gifts

Presents in pile #3.

From Fall to Winter

2 – 3 – 6 – 1 – 4; picture 5 does not fit, because swallows spend the winter in the south.

Star Points

Monica made the star with the fewest points (seventh from left, with only 4 points) and Mark made the star with the most points (third down from the top, with 8 points).

Where Is the Reindeer?

Self-Service

A/3; B/5; C/1; D/2; E/4

Decorating the Christmas Tree

Balthasar, one of the Three Magi.

The Snowman's Hat

Pot #7.

A Sweet Job

The cookies with the numbers 9, 11, 20, 24, and 36 add up to 100.

Cookie Dough

Dough #3.

John's Christmas Wish

Guitar #8.

Amazing Violins

The Leaping Seal

Seal #5.

Skating Elks

Four Skaters

The penguin on the left and one on the right at the top.

The Sled

Identical Squares

Beginning with the hockey-playing snowman:

A/4 – B/1;

F/2 – C/4;

H/1 – D/7.

Tree Slalom

The second runner from the left is the only one to ski the course without mistakes.

Who Shot the Goal?

Jim.

The Big Snowball Fight

Greg fights with Alice, Peter with Hannah, Eve with Will, Bob with Paul, Susanne with Ken, George with Phillip.

Downhill Skiers

Let's Hit the Slopes

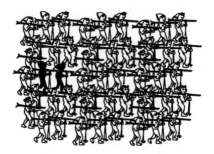

Six Snowballs

In the top snowball.

Snowman Mountain

You can build only five snowmen, because there are only five pots.

Bank Robbery

Carnival Game

There are several possible solutions. One of them: Throw the ball into holes 8, 12, 17 and 23.

RRRRocket

Venus.

Lucky Hit

Hal.

The Jester's Hat

Decoration #4.

Where Is My Mask?

Mask #8.

Calculating with 2 Clowns

The clown on top attended 77 costume parties, while the clown on the bottom attended 85.

Russian Doll

Butterflies

Butterfly #4.

Three Faces....

Through the Hedge

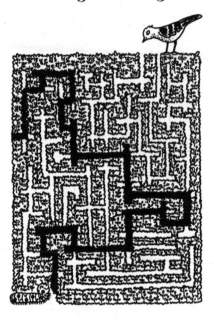

Elephant Watch

The Centipede

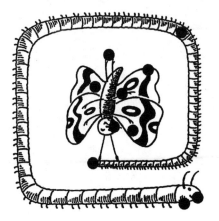

Egg Fraud

Snail, turtle, crocodile.

Rabbit Company

Rabbit #6.

Where Are the Rabbits?

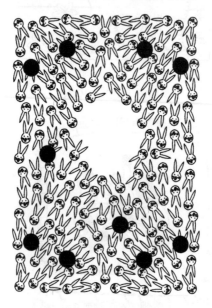

Look for 15 Differences!

A Museum Piece

The vase is 92 years old.

The Giant Egg

Painting Easter Eggs

Vickie 5   Jeff 3

David 3   Paula 1

Frog Tuba

Mouthpiece #2.

Who Is Riding?

Exchanging Ears

A/5; B/7; C/1; D/3; E/9; F/6; G/4; H/2; I/8.

Who Is Older?

The engine on top is 62 years old and the one on the
bottom is 59 years old.

Going Swimming

Picture #5.

Crocodile Snack

Crocodile D.

Crocodile in Love

The fifth crocodile from the top.

The Thirsty Biker

Path #2.

School Bus

Part 4.

Sorting Luggage

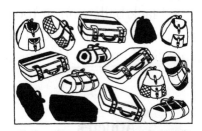

Ear Science

1. Elephant   2. Tiger

3. Chimpanzee   4. Lynx

6. Rhinoceros   7. Rabbit

8. Dachshund   9. Pig

10. Fox

Ear-pair #5 is left, and it belongs to a bat.

Who Won?

The team with the black balls won. It took five balls
(4 + 6 + 9 + 15 + 16) to add up to 50. The team with
the white balls needed four balls for that (10 + 11 + 14
+ 15).

Athletes

A/9; B/2; C/8; D/4; E/7; F/3; G/10; H/1; J/6; K/5.
The golfer is the only one left with no equipment.

Number Spectacular

90 divided by 6 = 15; 15 x 3 = 45.

The Bird

The bird ate 62 cherries, but sang only 61 songs.

Who Lives Here?

Dog #3 lives in the doghouse.

Lone Fish

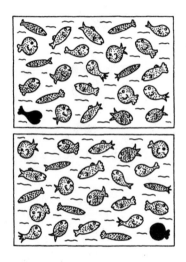

Twins in the Pond

Mary and Pat are twins, and ponds 2 and 10 are identical.

The Knight's Shield

The Tower

Piece #6 is left over.

OPTICAL ILLUSIONS

NOW YOU SEE IT . . .

What's this?

An elegant vase or two old men?

FIVE FIELDS

Here are five fields.

Which is the largest and which is the smallest in area?

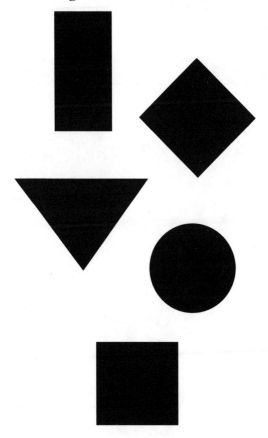

BLOCKBUSTER

This white block is a little bigger

than this white block.

—Isn't it?

EYE TEASER

Which line is bigger:
A or **B**?

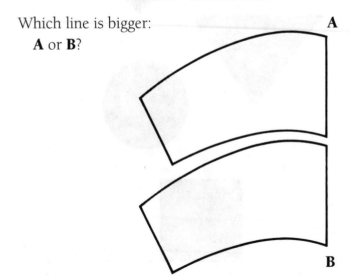

INS AND OUTS

Look carefully at the diagonal line on the facing page.
Is it straight? Or does it twist in and out of the
horizontal lines and seem a little jagged?

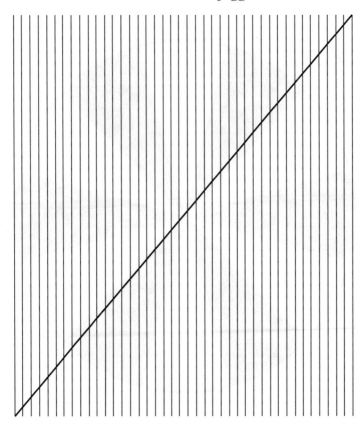

AROUND . . .

Look at *either* the circle on this page or the one on the
next.

Concentrate on it and revolve the book. Turn it
around and around as quickly as you can.

... AND AROUND

When you stop, for a moment the pattern will suddenly seem to go in the opposite direction.

X MARKS THE SPOT

Focus on the spot marked **X** and you will find that the dots in the square on the left appear in horizontal rows while the dots in the square on the right appear in vertical columns.

It will always happen that way—never the other way around!

RIGHT ANGLE?

Which is larger:
  Angle **A** or angle **B**?

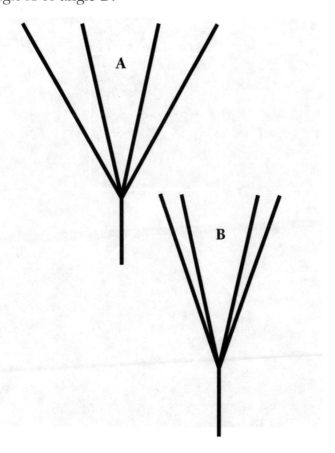

DIAMONDS AND SQUARES

Which is bigger:
The diamond or the square?

EYE DAZZLER

Look at this page for long enough and your mind will really begin to boggle.

What can you see? Rows of triangles? Rows of squares? Rows of open boxes seen from above? Or a mixture of different patterns that keep changing as you look at them?

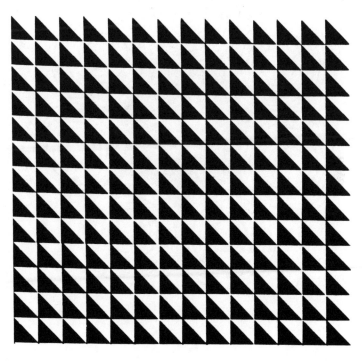

COG IN THE MIDDLE

Holding the page flat in front of you, move the book in a circle clockwise. What happens to the outside circles? What happens to the cogwheel in the middle?

SQUARE WORLD

Is one of these two areas very slightly larger than the other?

Which one?

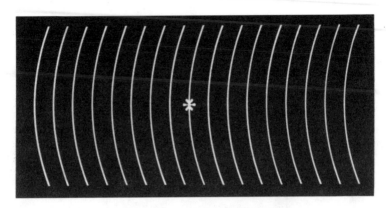

WATCH 'EM BEND!

Look at the star above steadily while you count to 100 very slowly.

Now look at the star below and watch the lines curve in the opposite direction!

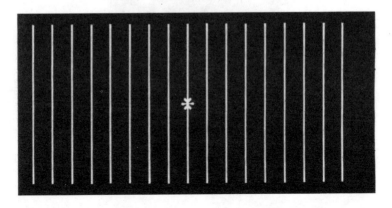

IMPOSSIBLE!

Look at the figure below.

Whichever way you look at it, this is an "impossible" object.

That is, it is possible to *draw* it on paper, but you could never *build* it out of cardboard or wood.

If it looks perfectly all right to you, look again— starting at the base of the object and then letting your eye move up it.

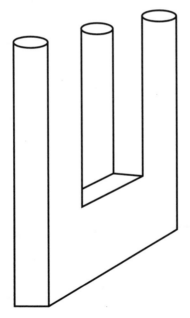

A QUESTION OF LINES

Which of the three horizontal lines is the longest: the top one, the middle one, or the bottom one?

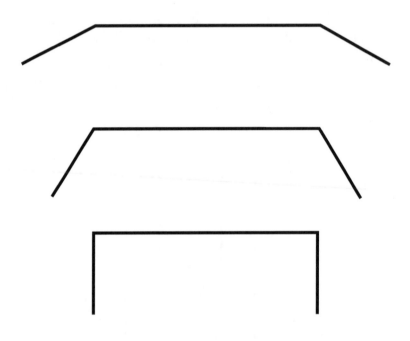

A QUESTION OF ANGLES

Which is the longer line:
   the one from **A** to **C**
            or
   the one from **B** to **D**?

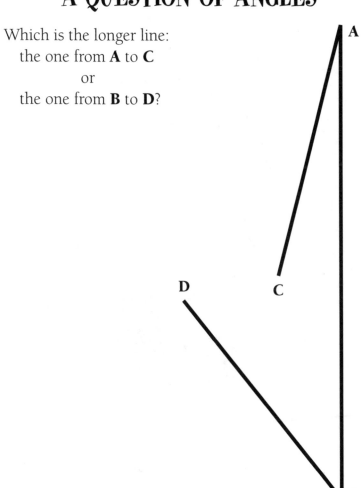

PORTRAIT OF A LADY

What can you see in this picture?

Is it a drawing of a very old lady? Or is it a picture of a young woman with her head turned slightly away from you?

UPSTAIRS DOWNSTAIRS

Find the top step. When (and if) you find it, start looking for the bottom step!

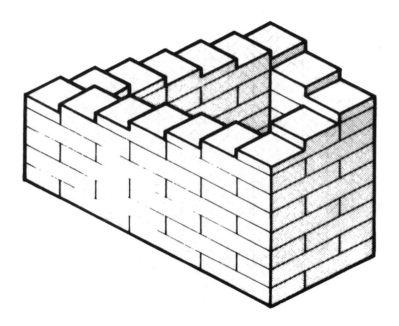

BULL'S-EYE

Revolve these pages, and the spirals will seem to get bigger or smaller, depending upon which direction you are turning the book.

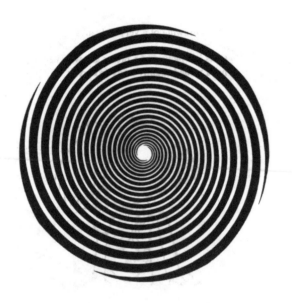

THE SKINNY SHIMMY

How many of the vertical lines on this page are bending this way and that? And how many of them are perfectly straight?

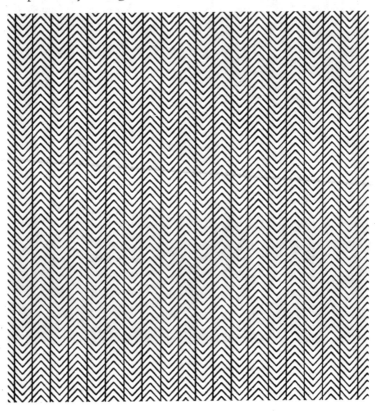

HOW FAR THIS TIME?

Is the distance between **A** and **B** greater or smaller than the distance between **C** and **D**?

MASTER CARPENTER

Ask some friends if they can build this hollow crate for you from 12 pieces of wood. Tell them they can have $1,000 if they succeed!

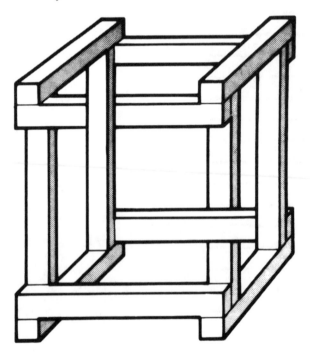

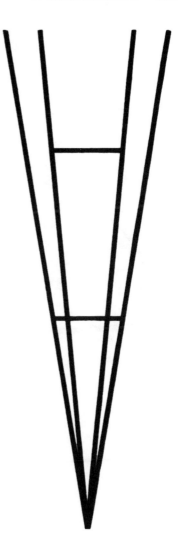

POINT OF VIEW

Look carefully at the two
horizontal lines.
 Which one is longer:
the top one or the
bottom one?

A CURVE BALL

Which of the three arcs is the biggest:
  the top one,
      the middle one,
          or the bottom one?

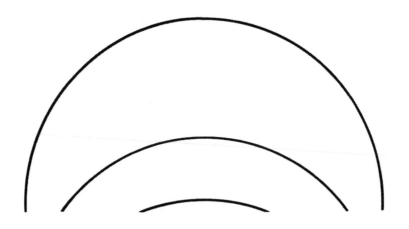

FROM HERE TO THERE

Is the line from **A** to **B** longer

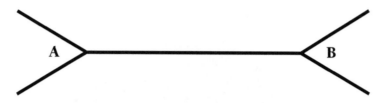

or shorter than the line from **C** to **D**?

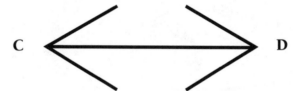

WHERE ARE YOU?

Are you up in the sky looking down on the roof of a house? Or are you in a room looking into a corner?

WHICH END IS UP?

Here's an unusual tube. Look carefully at it for at least a minute and then decide if you are looking down the tube from above it or up the tube from under it.

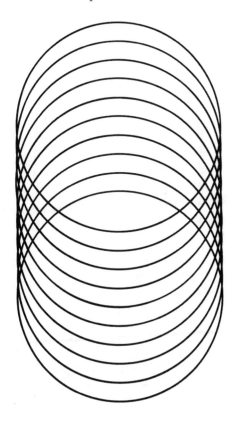

COUNTDOWN

How many cubes can you count here?

And if you found that mind-boggling, you can really get yourself confused by trying to find your way through the cube maze. Using tracing paper, go in at one arrow and come out the other.

CRISSCROSS

Glance at this page and strange gray spots will appear at all the points where the lines cross. Look at any one crossing in particular and the gray spot that was there will suddenly disappear!

GREAT OR SMALL?

Which of the two circles is larger?
  The one on this page?

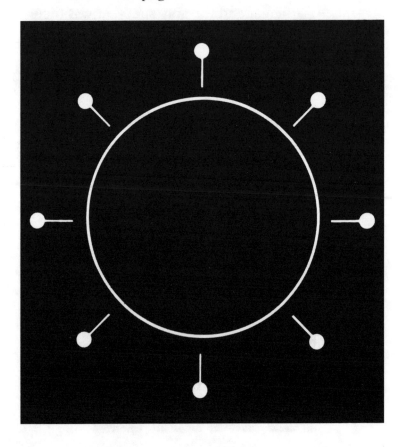

Or the one on this page?

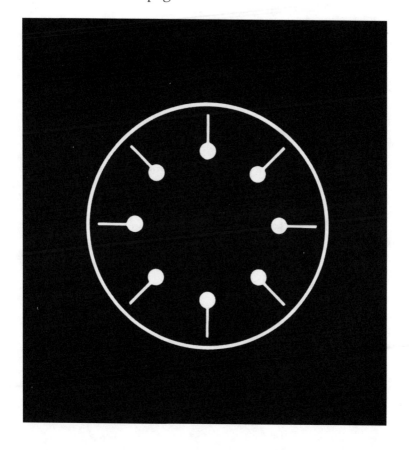

PARALLEL BARS

Look carefully at the parallelogram below.
Which line is longer: **AB** or **AC**?

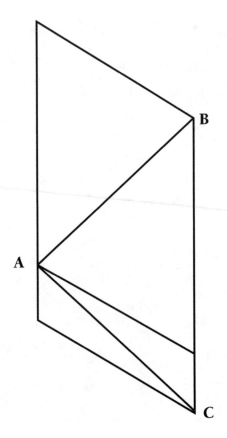

STRANGE CIRCLES

Which of the three rings is a perfect circle?

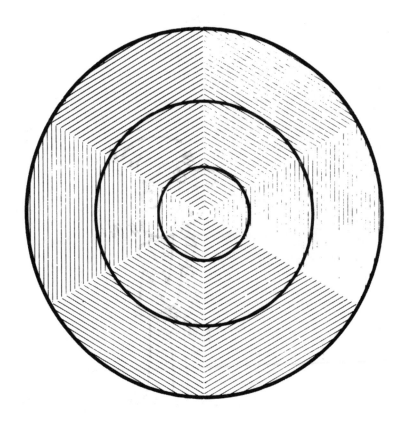

TOPSY TURVY

Look carefully at this picture by the great Dutch artist Verbeek—then turn it upside down and give yourself a surprise.

Just as he reaches a small grassy point of land, another fish attacks him, lashing furiously with his tail.

FAIR AND SQUARE

Of the three squares, which one is the smallest?

TURN, TURN, TURN

Look at the circle below and keep looking at it.

As you look at it, it will seem to revolve. (Don't look at it for too long, or you might begin to feel a little dizzy!)

WOODEN TRIANGLE

If you're any good at carpentry, try making this simple wooden triangle.

HONEYCOMB

Look at this pattern long enough and you'll find the circles begin to look like hexagons!

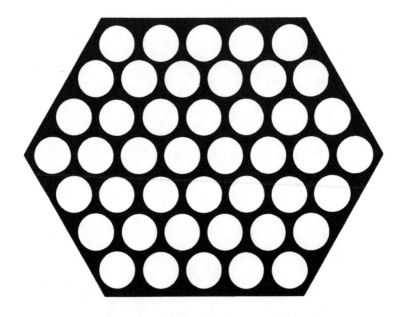

THICK AND THIN

Of the two thin lines, which is longer?

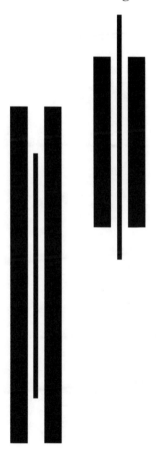

SQUARING THE CIRCLE

Which of the two circles is larger?

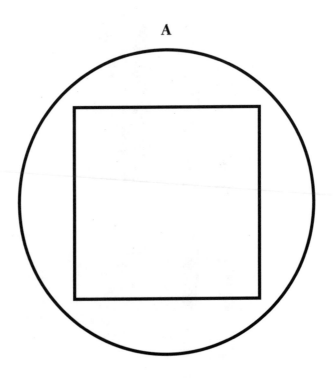

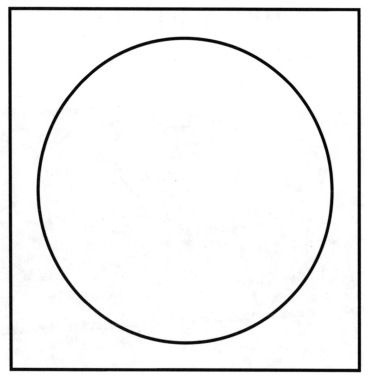

B

THE LONG AND SHORT OF IT

Which of the two horizontal lines is longer? It looks like the top one, but are you **sure**?

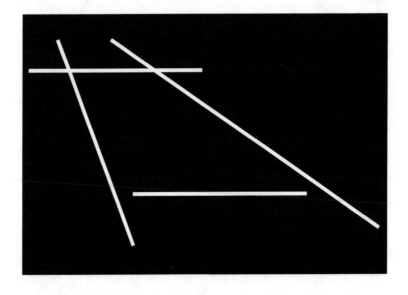

"E" IS FOR EYE-POPPING

Is this letter "E" toppling forward or sinking down?
Look at it steadily for half a minute.

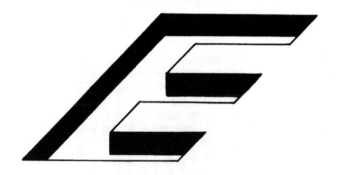

OUTSTANDING HAT

Here's a high hat. How much greater is its height than its width?

It's also an amazing maze! Use tracing paper and try to draw a path from one arrow to the other.

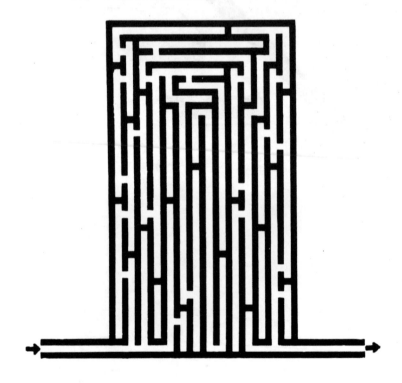

STRAPHANGER SIBLINGS

These are twin brothers, but one of them has a bigger appetite. Which one?

THE HOLE TRUTH

John P. Cubic was placed on the witness stand to be questioned about his puzzle-solving abilities. Of course, he declared himself a skilled puzzle-ologist. To prove it, he presented a cardboard square with an off-center hole.

Cubic claimed that by cutting this cardboard into only two pieces, he could move the hole into the center of this square. Can you figure out his cutting pattern?

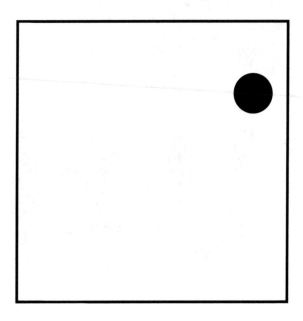

INSIDE OUTSIDE

Is the outside circle of **A** smaller than the inside circle of **B**?

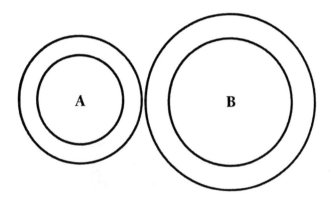

POPCORN, ANYONE?

Which of these moviegoers is the tallest?

LOTS OF DOTS

In this crowd of dots, there are five in the shape of a cross. Can you pick them out?

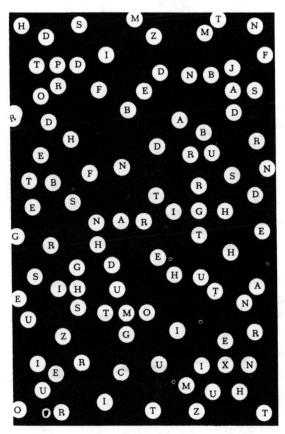

IT'S A THIN LINE

Are the thin lines parallel to each other? Or crooked?

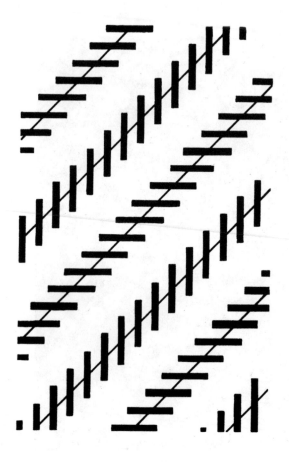

STRAIGHT AND NARROW?

Are the vertical lines straight?

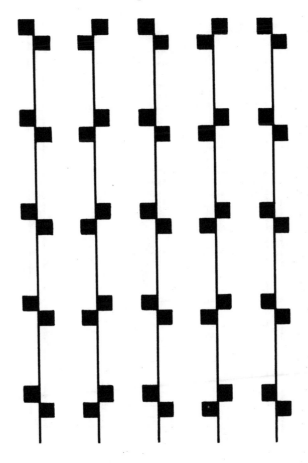

THE HIGHS AND LOWS

Is the left side of this picture high, or the right side?

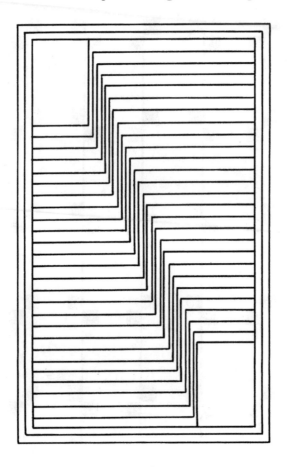

WHAT IS THIS?

Are you looking inside a tube? Or at the top of a beach ball?

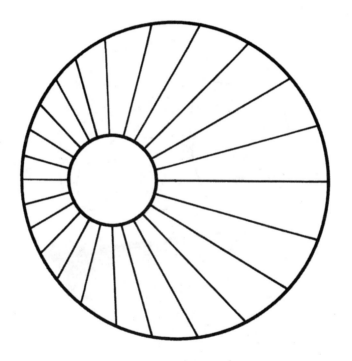

INVESTIGATE THIS

Each of these detectives obviously enjoys wearing a different style of hat. But which detective has the largest mouth?

A

B

C

D

CLIPS AND PINS

Which is the longest object in this picture?

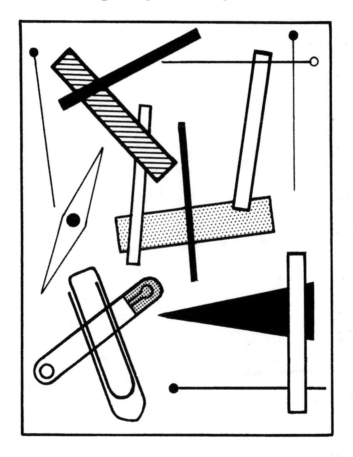

HIDDEN SHAPES

Take a look at each shape on these four pages. Would you believe it if anyone told you that you wouldn't be able to find that shape again—even though you were looking right at it?

Shape A

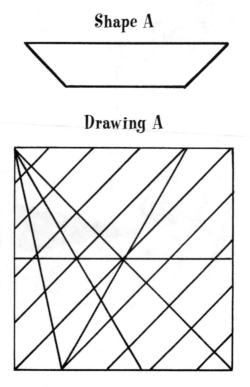

Drawing A

Each of these drawings shows how difficult it can be to see familiar shapes and figures when they are in unfamiliar surroundings. Each shape is hidden once (at the same size) inside its corresponding drawing. Can you find the shapes with your naked eye? Try this without using paper and pencil—at first!

Shape B   **Drawing B**

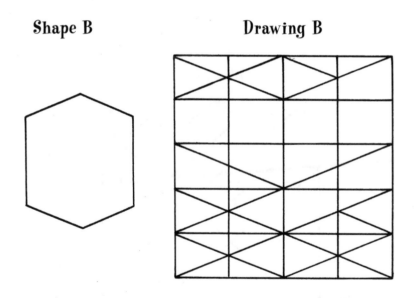

Shape C

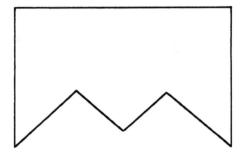

Drawing C

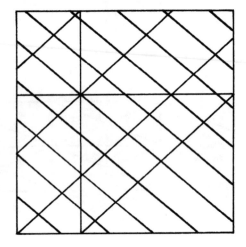

Shape D

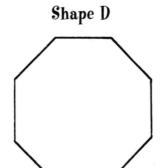

Drawing D

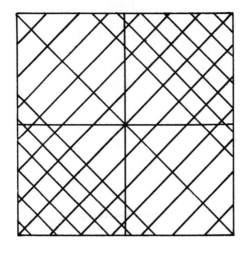

A DECORATOR'S DILEMMA, MAYBE!

One window has vertical slats. The other has Venetian blinds. Which window is taller …

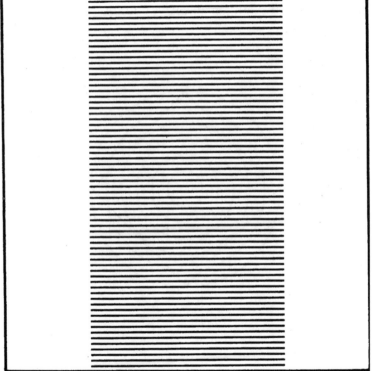

... and which is wider?

SQUARE DANCING

The next few pages present many different ways to view a square. Step one in the dance: Is the angular shape among the circles an exact square—or are its sides collapsing?

Are the horizontal lines parallel to each other?

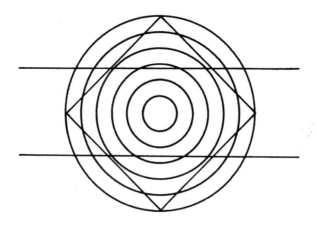

What is happening to the diamond shape?

Is this a perfect square?

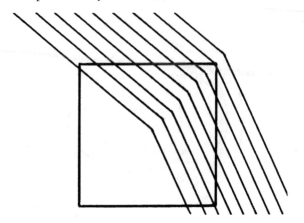

Are the sides of this square bulging out?

How many squares are there in the drawings on this page?

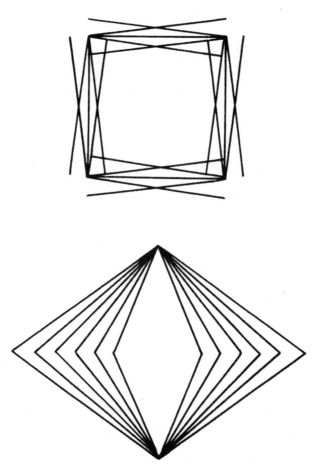

Are the sides of this square caving in?

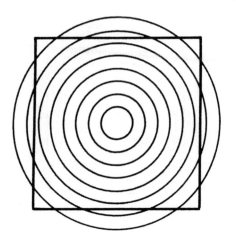

CIRCLE SURROUNDED

What is the matter with this circle?

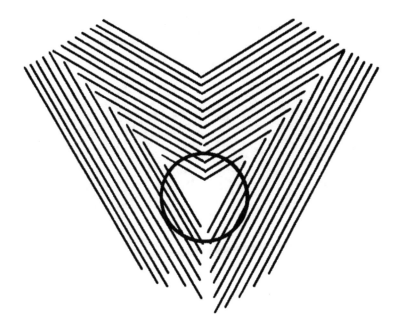

FLAT-TOP OR BUZZ CUT?

Isn't this circle flat at the top?

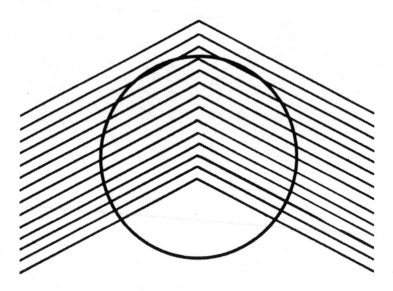

SEEING ISN'T EVERYTHING

After the light impressions are gathered and sent to the brain, our minds try to put them together into something understandable. We want it to make sense, to be familiar, to be safe, so we can go on about our business.

We do this automatically—even if parts of a picture are not connected, even if parts of it are missing!—until we perceive a harmonious, satisfying "whole" that makes sense to us.

Once we find a familiar pattern, it's difficult to break up the idea, to separate its parts. The new form can become an optical illusion—such as those shown on the next few pages. We can't concentrate on just part of it because our imaginations keep putting back what we try to block out of our minds!

For the first puzzle in this section, take a look at these circles:

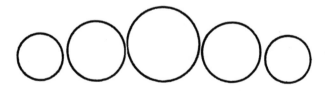

Do they sit on level ground, or do they arch upward?

Although parts of this picture are missing, our imaginations draw them in.

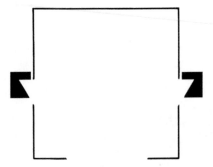

What white shape seems to be placed in front of the square?

HOW HIGH THE MOON?

Which moon seems larger, the one at the horizon or
the one high in the sky?

CIRCULAR LOGIC

The puzzles on the next few pages all involve circles. To start, which inner circle is larger— this one …

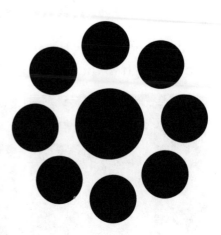

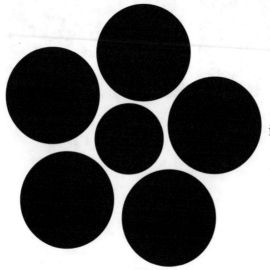

… or this inner circle?

Which circle is the largest?

Which of these circles are
the same size, those in
row **A** or those in row **B**?

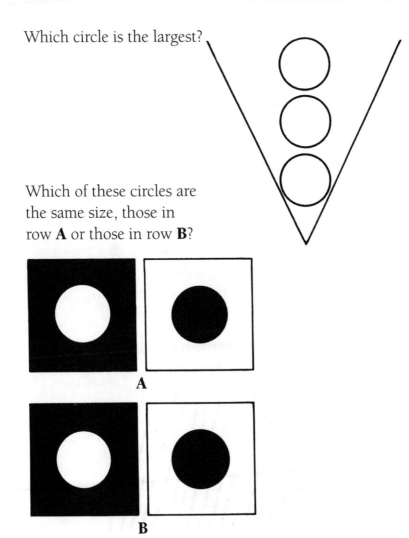

A

B

AFTERIMAGES

After you concentrate on a picture for a while, your eyes get tired. The most tired parts are certain spots on the retina, the part of the eye that contains light-sensitive cells. The brightest tones cause the greatest stress to these cells, which gradually become less sensitive to light.

When you look away from the picture and focus on a sheet of blank white paper, the nerve ends that are **less** tired will lightly reproduce the darker sections of the picture. Your eye transforms a negative into a positive!

You can check out afterimages and other similar effects in the puzzles on the following pages …

Concentrate for a while on the slanting lines. Then shift to the vertical lines on the next page. What do you see?

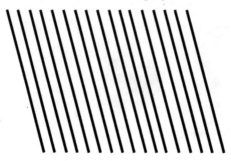

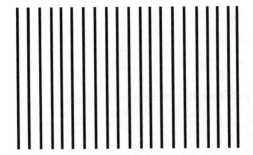

Concentrate very hard on a point in the white field of intersecting lines for about 30 seconds, then quickly shift your attention to one of the black squares. What do you see inside the black squares?

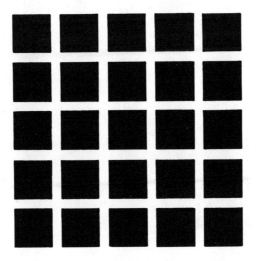

Will the single square at the top left fit into the black space between the two squares at the bottom—and between the two on the right?

Are these pointed arches continuous or broken?

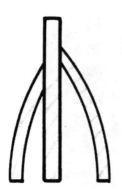
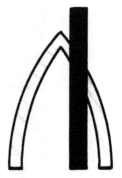

LITTLE THINGS MEAN A LOT

The first thing we see in any picture is usually the most obvious, most striking part. We often overlook smaller things, even though they may hold the key to a more important pattern.

The designs on the next couple pages have been put together from geometric forms.

For example, this pattern

has been created from this shape

Can you tell which simple shape forms the basis for the other patterns?

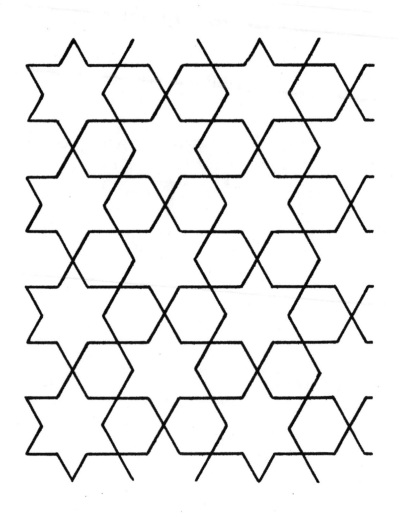

BACK AND FORTH, UP AND DOWN

Some scientists say it is "easier" to figure the distance between two points that lie on a horizontal level than those on vertical lines.

We can guess the distance from house to house, for example, or tree to tree—far more accurately than the distance between a house and a plane that just appeared on the horizon. Others say we've had more experience with horizontal distances and there is less we have to take into account.

Usually we overestimate vertical distances, even if they are just printed on the paper in front of us.

Try your eye on some ups and downs in the pages that follow …

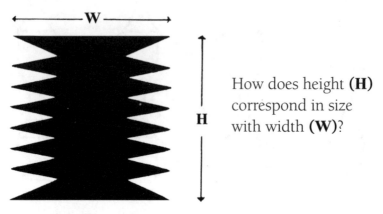

How does height **(H)** correspond in size with width **(W)**?

Is the dot midway between the point and the base of this triangle—or is it too high up?

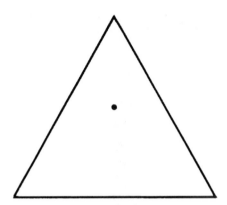

Which lines are the same length?

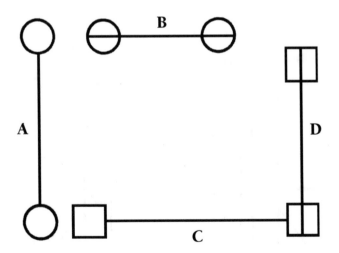

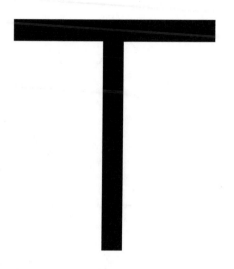

Which is longer—
the vertical or the
horizontal part of
the T?

In the left-hand figure, is the diagonal line straight? In
the right-hand figure, which line is the continuation of
A? Is it **B**, or is it **C**?

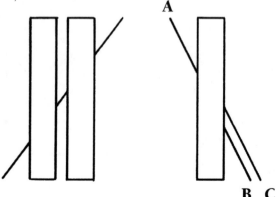

Is the center line **A** shorter than …

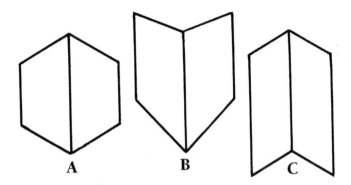

… the other center lines in **B** through **F**?

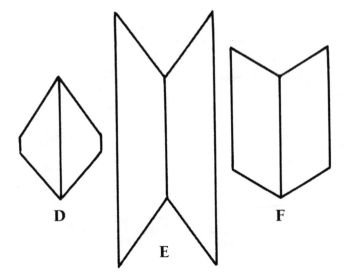

CURVES AHEAD!

Watch out for the curves coming up! Can you navigate the following pages and answer these questions correctly?

Are **A** and **B** the same size?

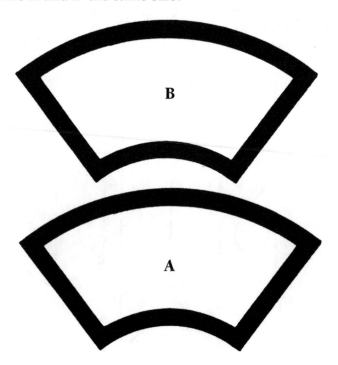

Are the lined-in sections **(B)** of the circle larger than the open sections **(A)**?

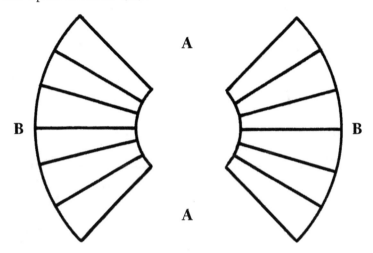

Is **A**-to-**A** the same length as **B**-to-**B**?

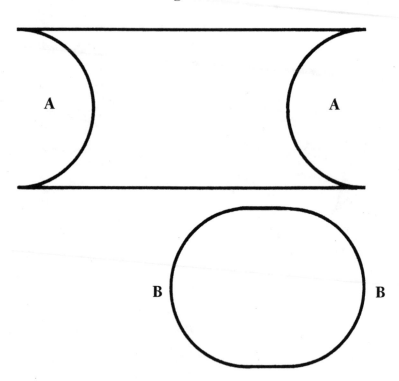

Which glass has a wider base?

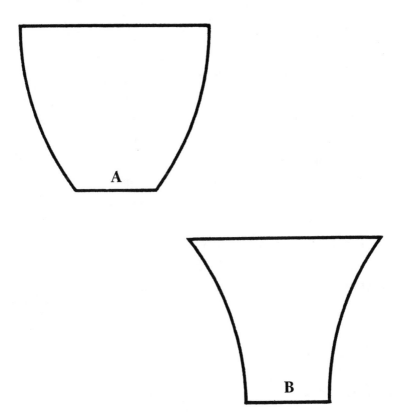

COSMIC FLOWER

Take a look at the way this design pulsates. This is why: When you look at anything that is close to you, the muscles around your eyes pull into a spherical shape to get the words and pictures in focus. But because the lens of your eye isn't perfectly round, some parts of what you're looking at will be in focus and others will look blurry.

Normally, these differences in the clarity of your vision are on the outer edge of the object you're looking at, so you can still read the words and recognize the pictures. But in an illusion such as this one—where all the lines come from different angles and meet at the center—it is impossible for you to focus clearly on all of it at once.

Your eyes are always making tiny movements that you cannot prevent, no matter how hard you try. So the clear parts of the design and the blurry parts are constantly changing. This is called "optical distortion," and it's what makes the picture seem to move, shimmer, swirl or pulsate!

SHIMMERING SQUARES

The shimmering effect you see in this illusion is caused by optical distortion. This illusion is unusual because all the lines in it are sloped forward 45° or backward 135° degrees. Try the following experiment to see why this helps make the illusion interesting:

Concentrate on one of the rows of lines that are sloped at 45°. You'll find that all the squares formed by these lines appear steady, while the squares formed by lines sloping backward at 135° look blurry and faint, and seem to shimmer.

Then concentrate on a row of lines sloped at 135° and you'll see that all the squares formed with lines sloped at 45° will look blurry and seem to shimmer. This effect occurs because your eyes cannot focus on all of the illusion at once. The parts that you do focus on will appear clear, while the other parts will look blurry.

ALL SQUARE

This optical illusion is especially puzzling. If you study it closely, the ovals in the middle first seem to bulge out and then seem to recede.

The reason they change is that when your eyes scan the design from left to right, the position of the ovals suggests to your brain that the ovals are popping out. But then your eyes go back over the picture.

With so many different ways to scan the illusion—and no clues to which way is "right"—you may see the ovals recede or do any number of other interesting tricks.

MAKING WAVES

When you stare at this optical illusion for a while, the curved lines seem to form the crests and valleys of the waves. They may even seem to move a little.

If you stare some more—until your eyes get tired—you may also see phantom lines of color (especially in bright light) where the curved lines run parallel to each other, between the valleys and crests of the waves.

The restless motion of the waves in this illusion is caused by optical distortion.

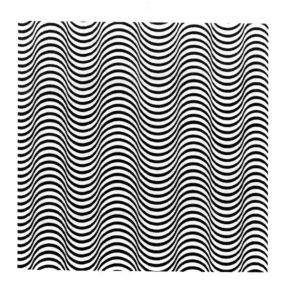

JESTER

If you look at this circular checkerboard closely, it will seem to pulsate and shimmer. You may also see the black-and-white patches line up to form petals of a flower.

The shimmering is caused by optical distortion. But the petals formed by your brain are an example of another phenomenon called "good continuation."

This happens because your brain is trying to make sense out of what it sees. It seeks out shapes or patterns that it recognizes. Sometimes it works so hard and so cleverly that it imagines an object that isn't really there.

And then we have an optical illusion!

TRICKY TILES

What makes this design vibrate? Right! It's optical distortion again. The repetition of the same design on each tile helps to make this illusion even more effective.

ZINNIA

Here you may see some gray or white spots at the points where the black lines meet. This is caused by your eyes' response to dark and light. You may also see that the imaginary dots "link up" to form a series of circles that radiate out from the middle of the illusion—another example of good continuation!

THE ESCALATOR

When you look closely at this illusion, you may get the impression that the horizontal panels are moving—with a tiny jerking motion—and the central panel may seem to be unexpectedly bright.

The reason that the "Escalator" seems to move is that you can't keep your eyes perfectly still, no matter how hard you try, and as your eyes move about, so does the image in the illusion!

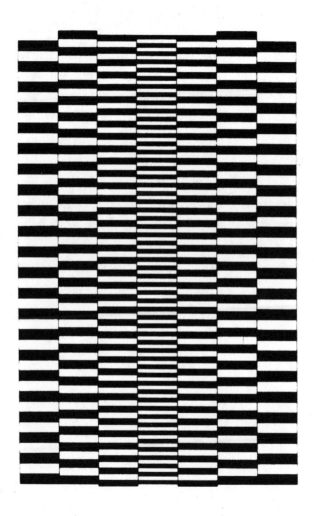

CHRYSANTHEMUM

When you look at this design, you get the impression that it is not flat, but three-dimensional. Some parts of the illusion appear higher, and some lower—which gives the impression of depth.

However, if you look at the curved lines that define the bumps and hollows of the flower, you will find a curious situation: Look at the curve that defines the outer edge of the flower and follow it right around the circle. In some places the curved lines seem to define a hump, and in others, a hollow.

This object could not exist in three dimensions. Along with being another shimmering example of optical distortion, "Chrysanthemum" is an example of an impossible figure.

THE TEMPLE

This is a reversing figure that can be looked at as a pyramid viewed from above, with the smallest square forming the top—or as a passageway leading toward a tiny square door. If you look steadily at this illusion, you will probably see it flash betwen these two images!

HIDDEN PICTURES

The picture puzzles in this section come from *Cole's Funny Picture Book*, by Edward William Cole and published in the 1800s. Cole's book contains all sorts of stories, rhymes and pictures. But the most interesting things in the book are the picture puzzles—the best of which are reprinted here.

These pictures may look ordinary, but they're really great examples of the art of illusion. If you didn't know that there were pictures hidden inside the pictures, you'd probably never know what you were missing.

Here is the showman and his learned dog. Where is his wife?

This road leads up to the giant's castle.
Where is the giant?

Mother Hubbard is serving tea to her children, but five of them are missing. Can you find them?

The rats are hiding from this cat. Can you find where they have gone?

This is a faithful Newfoundland dog, but where, oh where, is his master?

The queen is searching everywhere. Will she ever find the king?

ANSWERS

Page 152

It's both, of course. Concentrate on the white area and you'll see the vase. Concentrate on the black, and the two men will appear.

Page 153

All five fields have exactly the same area. The different shapes make them appear to be different sizes.

Page 154

No. Both blocks are the same size. If they look unequal in size, it's because of the different black lengths on either side of them.

Page 154

If you figured that they're both the same size, you're correct!

Page 155

The diagonal line is quite straight. The vertical lines behind it make it seem distorted.

Page 159

The angles are the same! They **look** unequal because of the other angles on either side of them, which are different.

Page 160

They're equal, but the tilted square seems larger.

Page 161

All of these effects can be seen in this image.

Page 162

The circles spin to the right. Many people say the cogwheel turns to the left; others say it stands still.

Page 163

The white square seems a little larger than the black square, but in fact, they're exactly the same size.

Page 166

All three are the same length. It is the **angles** that make the horizontal lines look like different lengths.

Page 167

Both lines are the same length. Once again, it is the angles the lines make that cause them to look unequal.

Page 168

It's both. Look at the picture long enough, and you'll see the old lady at one moment and the girl the next.

Page 169

If you think you managed to find the top and bottom steps, you are wrong. They don't exist, because this stairway is an impossibility!

Page 172

They are **all** perfectly straight. It is the pattern of wavy lines behind them that makes them appear to bend.

Page 173

It looks greater, but in fact it's the same.

Page 174

Don't worry, your money's safe. No matter how skilled your friends may be in carpentry, they will never be able to build this crate. It's an **impossible object**.

Page 175

Both are exactly the same length. It's the difference in position that makes the lower one **look** longer.

Page 176

All three are arcs from **the same circle**, but the more you see of each arc, the greater the curve seems to be.

Page 177

It **looks** longer, but both lines are actually the same length.

Page 178

The answer is "either." The line in the middle will either appear nearer to you (the roof) or farther away from you (the corner)—depending on how **you** see it!

Page 179

You can look at the tube either way. Sometimes you'll feel you're seeing through it from the top, and sometimes from the bottom!

Page 180

The answer is six or seven. It will be six if you saw the patterned part as the **top** of each cube, but seven if you saw the patterned part as the bottom of each cube.

The path out of the maze is shown here:

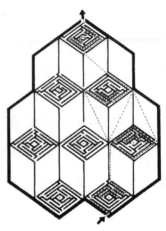

Page 182

You may be wrong! The one on page 183 certainly **looks** smaller, but in fact both circles are identical in size.

Page 184

AB **looks** a lot longer, but both lines are the same length. Check with a ruler if you don't believe it.

Page 185

All three are! It is the background pattern that makes the perfect circles seem distorted.

Page 187

The three squares are identical. The ones with the vertical and horizontal lines in them just seem to occupy a larger area.

Page 189

You can't do it! The wooden triangle is one of those "impossible objects."

Page 191

The two thin lines are of equal lengths.

Page 192

A looks a little larger than **B**, but both circles are the same size.

Page 194

Both horizontal lines are the same length. It's the converging lines that make the top line look longer.

Page 195

Both are possible. It depends on how you look at it.

Page 196

The height of the hat and the width of the brim are identical—vertical lines often seem longer than horizontal lines of the same length. Here's the solution to the maze:

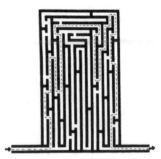

Page 197

There's no way to tell. The twin with the horizontal stripes seems to be fatter, but he really isn't. Our eyes follow the lines in his suit, so the twin on the right seems broader and shorter than his brother.

Page 198

1) Cut out an L-shaped section of the square like this:

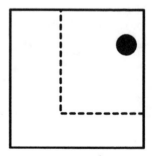

2) Rotate the cutout L-shape to the opposite corner of the piece with the hole.

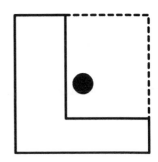

Page 199

No, but it seems to be because **B** is in a larger area.

Page 200

They are all the same height. The man at the right looks tallest. We expect things to look smaller when they are farther away. The man at the right is farthest away, and we would expect him to look the smallest. Since he doesn't, we assume he's really larger than the others.

Page 201

The dot-shaped cross is just to the right of the center of the diagram. It spells out "R-I-G-H-T." It may take you a while to find it because the other dots distract your attention.

Page 202

Exactly parallel. The thicker cross-hatch lines just give the illusion that they are bending. Some scientists say this is because we can't judge the size of angles well. Others say the cross-lines distract us.

Page 203

Yes, they run parallel to each other.

Page 204

Depending on the way you look at it, either side.

Page 205

Either!

Page 206

The four detectives have equally large mouths.

Page 207

All the objects are the same length!

Page 208

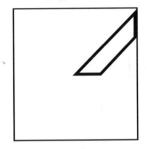

Page 209

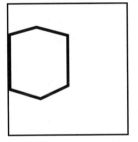

Page 210

Page 211

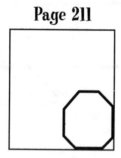

Page 212

They are both the same height and width. The one with the horizontal stripes looks wider because your eyes follow the horizontal lines.

Page 214

It is an exact square, but when it is broken by other lines, our eyes are distracted and follow the new lines instead of the original square.

Page 215

Yes. The other lines distract from them and make them seem to bend a little, but they are parallel.

Page 215

Nothing. It is a perfect square, tipped on its side, but the distracting boxes make it seem warped.

Page 216

Yes.

Page 216

No. Our eyes cannot separate the figure from the intercepting arcs. Nevertheless, it is a perfect square.

Page 217

There is one exact square.

Page 217

Same.

Page 218

No, but the circle makes it look that way.

Page 219

Absolutely nothing. It is an exact circle.

Page 220

No. It's a perfect circle.

Page 221

They all sit on level ground.

Page 222

A triangle with equal sides.

Page 223

They are the same size. Scientists tell us that we still see the sky as a kind of flattened dome, nearer to us than the horizon—even though we know better. When any object is close to the horizon, we assume it is farther away than when it is overhead. Therefore, while the moon is always the same size, we trick ourselves into thinking that it is larger when it is near the horizon.

Page 224

The inner circles are the same size, although the bottom circle looks smaller.

Page 225

They are all the same size.

Page 225

In row **A** both circles are the same size, but the white one seems larger. When bright light falls on the retina of our eyes (where the nerve cells are), more nerve fibers react than actually had the light hit them. This causes a "spreading" effect, making the light object seem larger. In row **B** the black circle is actually larger, although both circles seem to be the same size.

Page 226

The vertical lines seem to lean to the right.

Page 227

You see an even blacker lattice design inside the black squares! This is the result of your eyes being tired of seeing the white lines—so they record the black instead when you look away.

Page 228

The square fits into both spaces. It seems larger than the black space due to the "spreading" effect of light.

Page 228

Continuous. It is the solid bar in front of them that makes them look broken.

Page 230

Page 231

Page 232

Height and width are the same.

Page 233

It is exactly in the center.

Page 233

Line **A** equals **B** and **C** equals **D**. Line **A** seems longer than **B** because we unconsciously add the circles on the end of the line to its length. The same is true of line **C** with its open square.

Page 234

The lines are the same length, but the vertical one seems longer. Some scientists say that the horizontal line looks shorter simply because it has been broken into two parts.

Page 234

Left: Yes, but when you break a straight line with a solid bar, the straight line seems displaced.

Right: **B** is the continuation of **A**. **C** looks as though it connects with **A** because the solid bar "displaces" the line.

Page 235

The center lines in drawings **A** through **F** are all the same height. The only differences are the angles of the lines leading away from them.

Page 236

A seems larger, but they are both the same size. Our tendency is to compare the base of **B** with the top arch of **A**.

Page 237

The sections are all the same size—one-quarter of the whole circle.

Page 238

Yes, although **A**-to-**A** seems larger because it intersects a larger area.

Page 239

The glasses are equally wide at the base, but **A** seems longer because the glass is wider.

Page 255

The showman's wife is actually his dog! The dog's front legs form her legs, and the dog's fluffy tail forms her head.

Page 256

The houses at the top of the picture are built on top of the giant's nose, and the small forest to the right forms his eyebrows. The enclosure near the middle of the picture forms his ear, and the large patch of forest forms his beard.

Page 257

One child's face is hidden in the top of Mother Hubbard's hat. Another is hidden upside-down in the shoe, just above the tea tray. A third child's face can be seen below Mother Hubbard's shawl that wraps her shoulders, and a fourth bulges out of her apron, just below the bow tied around her waist. The last child is hidden in the hem of her apron!

Page 258

The rats have hidden their faces in the cat's ears.

Page 258

To find his master in the dog's face, turn the picture upside down. The man's bearded face is hidden on the lower part of the dog's face (between his nose and eye), and his hat is formed by one of the faithful pet's ears.

Page 259

The king has tumbled down behind her, with his head on the ground and his feet behind her head.

Index

Page Key: Puzzle, *Answer*

Afterimages, 226–228, *275–276*
All Square, 244
Amazing Violins, 54, *132*
. . . And Around, 157
Around…, 156
Athletes, 109, *148*
Back and Forth—Up and Down, 232–235, *277–278*
Bank Robbery, 70, *136*
Big Snowball Fight, The, 64, *135*
Bird, The, 112, *148*
Blockbuster, 154, *262*
Bull's-Eye, 170
Butterflies, 79, *138*
Calculating with 2 Clowns, 77, *137*
Camels, 20, *122*
Carnival Game, 72, *136*

Centipede, The, 84, *141*
Chrysanthemum, 252–253
Circle Surrounded, 219, *273*
Circular Logic, 224–225, *274–275*
Clips and Pins, 207, *270*
Cog in the Middle, 162, *263*
Cookie Dough, 52, *132*
Cosmic Flower, 240–241
Countdown, 180, *266*
Crazy About Bookmarks, 39, *128*
Crisscross, 181
Crocodile in Love, 100, *146*
Crocodile Snack, 99, *146*
Curve Ball, A, 176, *265*
Curves Ahead!, 236–239, *278*
Decorating the Christmas Tree, 48, *131*
Decorator's Dilemma, Maybe!, A, 212, *272*

Diamonds and Squares, 160, *263*

Down the Slide, 8, *119*

Downhill Skiers, 66, *135*

"E" Is for Eye-Popping, 195, *267*

Ear Science, 106, *147*

Egg Fraud, 86, *142*

Elephant Watch, 83, *141*

Escalator, The, 250–251

Exchanging Ears, 96, *145*

Eye Dazzler, 161, *263*

Eye, diagram of, 5

Eye Teaser, 154, *262*

Fair and Square, 187, *267*

Five Fields, 153, *262*

Flat-Top or Buzz Cut?, 220, 274

Four Skaters, 58, *133*

Four Triplets, 19, *122*

Frog Tuba, 94, *145*

From Fall to Winter, 43, *130*

From Here to There, 177, *265*

Gathering of the Ravens, 33, *127*

Giant Egg, The, 91, *143*

Gingerbread Dominoes, 41, *130*

Going Swimming, 98, *146*

Great or Small?, 182, *266*

Greetings from the Woodchuck, 28, *125*

Half a Crown, 22, *123*

Hat Heaven, 24, *124*

Hibernation, 32, *126*

Hidden Gifts, 42, *130*

Hidden Pictures, 255–259, *279–281*

Hidden Shapes, 208–211, *271–272*

Highs and Lows, The, 204, *270*

Hole Truth, The, 198, *268*

Home of the Fountain Pen, 35, *128*

Honeycomb, 190

How Far This Time?, 173, *264*

How High the Moon?, 223, *274*

How Old Is This Tree?, 30, *126*

Huge Hole, A, 11, *120*

Identical Squares, 60, *134*

Impossible!, 165

In the Hat Shop, 36, *128*

Ins and Outs, 155, *262*

Inside Outside, 199, *269*

Investigate This, 206, *270*

It's a Thin Line, 202, *270*

Jester, 246–247

Jester's Hat, The, 75, *137*

John's Christmas Wish, 53, *132*

Kite Festival, 18, *121*

Knight's Shield, The, 116, *150*

Leaping Seal, The, 55, *133*

Let's Hit the Slopes, 67, *135*

Little Things Mean a Lot, 229–231, *276*

Lone Fish, 111, *149*

Long and Short of It, The, 194, *267*

Long Tongues, 15, *120*

Look for 15 Differences!, 89, *143*

Looking for Footprints, 34, *127*

Looking for the Boomerang, 16, *121*

Lots of Dots, 201, *269*

Lucky Hit, 74, *137*

Making Waves, 245

Many Great-Smelling Gingerbreads, 40, *129*

Master Carpenter, 174, *264*

Museum Piece, A, 90, *143*

Mysterious Request, 26, *125*

New Eyeglasses, 23, *123*

Now You See It…, 152, *262*

Number Spectacular, 110, *148*

On a Gondola in Venice, 17, *121*

Optical Illusions, 151–281, *261–281*

Optical Puzzles, 7–117, *118–150*

Outstanding Hat, 196, 268

Painting Easter Eggs, 92, 144

Parallel Bars, 184, 266

Point of View, 175, 265

Popcorn, Anyone?, 200, 269

Portrait of a Lady, 168, 264

Potato Stamp, 38, 128

Question of Angles, A, 167, 264

Question of Lines, A, 166, 263

Rabbit Company, 87, 142

Right Angle?, 159, 263

Rock Climbing, 27, 125

RRRRocket, 73, 137

Russian Doll, The, 78, 138

School Bus, 103, 146

Seeing Isn't Everything, 221–222, 274

Self-Service, 47, 131

Shimmering Squares, 242–243

Six Snowballs, 68, 136

Skating Elks, 56, 133

Skinny Shimmy, The, 172, 264

Sled, The, 59, 134

Snowman Mountain, 69, 136

Snowman's Hat, The, 50, 131

Sorting Luggage, 104, 147

Square Dancing, 214–218, 272–273

Square World, 163, 263

Squaring the Circle, 192, 267

Star Points, 44, 130

Straight and Narrow?, 203, 270

Strange Circles, 185, 266

Straphanger Siblings, 197, 268

Sweet Job, A, 51, 132

Swimming Marathon, 10, 119

Temple, The, 254

Thick and Thin, 191, *267*

Thirsty Biker, The, 102, *146*

Three Faces . . ., 80, *139*

Through the Hedge, 82, *140*

Topsy Turvy, 186

Tower, The, 117, *150*

Tree Slalom, 62, *134*

Tricky Tiles, 248

Turn, Turn, Turn, 188

Twins in the Pond, 114, *149*

Upstairs Downstairs, 169, *264*

Visual system, 4–6

Wash Day, 25, *124*

Watch 'Em Bend!, 164

What Is This?, 205, *270*

Where Are the Rabbits?, 88, *142*

Where Are You?, 178, *265*

Where Is My Mask?, 76, *137*

Where Is My Wife?, 14, *120*

Where Is the Mouse?, 29, *126*

Where Is the Reindeer?, 46, *131*

Which 6 Objects…, 31, *126*

Which End Is Up?, 179, *265*

Who Is Flying Where?, 12, *120*

Who Is Older?, 97, *145*

Who Is Riding?, 95, *145*

Who Lives Here?, 113, *148*

Who Shot the Goal?, 63, *135*

Who Won?, 108, *148*

Wild River, 21, *123*

Wooden Triangle, 189, *267*

X Marks the Spot, 158

Zinnia, 249

WHAT IS MENSA?

Mensa—The High IQ Society

Mensa is the international society for people with a high IQ. We have more than 100,000 members in over 40 countries worldwide.

The society's aims are:
- to identify and foster human intelligence for the benefit of humanity;
- to encourage research in the nature, characteristics, and uses of intelligence;
- to provide a stimulating intellectual and social environment for its members.

Anyone with an IQ score in the top two percent of the population is eligible to become a member of Mensa—are you the "one in 50" we've been looking for?

Mensa membership offers an excellent range of benefits:
- Networking and social activities nationally and around the world;
- Special Interest Groups (hundreds of chances to pursue your hobbies and interests—from art to zoology!);
- Monthly International Journal, national magazines, and regional newsletters;
- Local meetings—from game challenges to food and drink;
- National and international weekend gatherings and conferences;
- Intellectually stimulating lectures and seminars;
- Access to the worldwide SIGHT network for travelers and hosts.

**For more information about
Mensa International:**

www.mensa.org
Mensa International
15 The Ivories
6–8 Northampton Street
Islington, London N1 2HY
United Kingdom

**For more information about
American Mensa:**

www.us.mensa.org
Telephone: (800) 66-MENSA
American Mensa Ltd.
1229 Corporate Drive West
Arlington, TX 76006-6103 US

**For more information about
British Mensa (UK and Ireland):**

www.mensa.org.uk
Telephone: +44 (0) 1902 772771
E-mail: enquiries@mensa.org.uk
British Mensa Ltd.
St. John's House
St. John's Square
Wolverhampton WV2 4AH
United Kingdom